Ann Summers

Raunchy and Rampant
GUIDE TO SEX TOYS

Ann Summers

Raunchy and Rampant
GUIDE TO SEX TOYS

EBURY
PRESS

First published in Great Britain in 2007

1 3 5 7 9 10 8 6 4 2

Text written by Siobhan Kelly © Ebury Press 2007
Photographs © John Freeman 2007

First published by Ebury Press
Random House, 20 Vauxhall Bridge Road, London SW1V 2SA

Random House Australia (Pty) Limited
20 Alfred Street, Milsons Point, Sydney, New South Wales
2061, Australia

Random House New Zealand Limited
18 Poland Road, Glenfield, Auckland 10, New Zealand

Random House South Africa (Pty) Limited
Endulini, 5A Jubilee Road, Parktown 2193, South Africa

The Random House Group Limited Reg. No. 954009
www.randomhouse.co.uk

A CIP catalogue record for this book is available from the
British Library

Art direction and design by Smith & Gilmour, London
Photography by John Freeman

ISBN: 9780091916435

Papers used by Ebury are natural, recyclable products made
from wood grown in sustainable forests.

Printed and bound in Singapore by Tien Wah Press

Designed and typeset by Smith & Gilmour, London

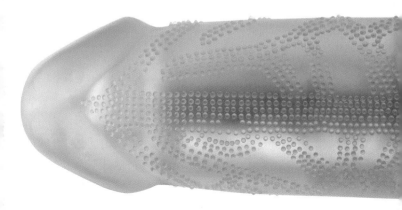

Introduction

Women love sex and they love sex toys. When I started 25 years ago, that statement was met with outrage and disbelief. Back then, most men thought that it was only them that liked sex! Thank goodness times have changed and today's generation have a much healthier attitude to sex, which is reflected in the fact that we sell over 2.5 million sex toys a year.

The one thing I get asked most often by women, is do we have a book that explains how to get the most from their sex toys. A book that will explain to the first-timer and the experienced sex-toy user alike, how to use each one, how it should make them feel, how they can use their toys with and in some cases on their partner, plus lots of tips from our experts on new and fun ways to play with your toys. Well, here it is. I hope you enjoy it as much as we've enjoyed compiling it for you!

Jacqueline Gold
Chief Executive of Ann Summers

PART 1
SEX ED

The inside info on your body and orgasms

To get the most out of your sex toys, it's vital that you know your way around your own anatomy. Sure, sure, you've been fiddling around down there ever since you first discovered something that was like a sneeze, only nicer – but how much do you really know about your genitals?

Ladies: welcome to your body

Women are more dependent than men on all-over body stimulation, and less likely to spend hours obsessing about their genitalia. So it's even more important that girls get to know the contents of their knickers.

The clitoris

Lucky girls! The clit is the only organ in the human body that exists entirely for pleasure. This word comes from the Greek word for 'key', appropriately, as this tiny bud of flesh is your sure-fire route to orgasm. You can find it under a tiny hood of skin at the top of the vulva, near where you pee. The only visible part is the tip, which looks like a tiny pinkish bud – but the blood vessels and nerve endings attached to it go back as far as 5cm, while the amazing sensations that occur when it's licked, caressed or buzzed ripple through the entire body, from head to toe.

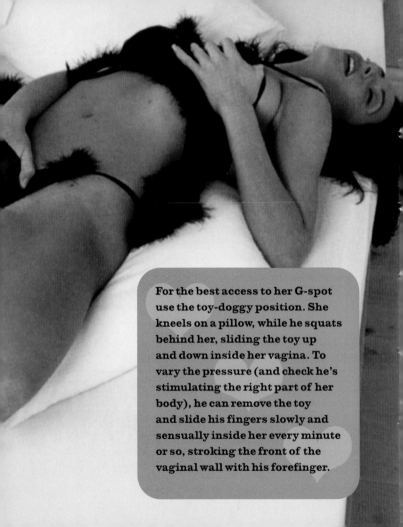

For the best access to her G-spot
use the toy-doggy position. She
kneels on a pillow, while he squats
behind her, sliding the toy up
and down inside her vagina. To
vary the pressure (and check he's
stimulating the right part of her
body), he can remove the toy
and slide his fingers slowly and
sensually inside her every minute
or so, stroking the front of the
vaginal wall with his forefinger.

Labia

The word labia is Latin for lips, and there are two sets that make up the vulva (the bits of the female front bottom you can see). The labia majora are the fleshy, outer lips where pubic hair grows. The labia minora are the hairless folds of skin on the inside and may or may not hang lower than the labia majora. Neither set of labia objects to being stroked by a vibrator on a low setting.

Vagina

This is the bit inside that you can't see. The long elastic muscular tube is the hostess for the penis during intercourse or a dildo or vibrator during solo play. During sexual arousal, it swells up with blood and produces mucus-like lubrication to allow the penis in. The bottom third of the vagina is the most sensitive to stimulation; the further up you go, the less the nerve endings can be stimulated.

G-spot

Named after Dr Ernst Grafenburg, the German gynaecologist who first identified it, the G-spot is a highly erogenous zone located about 5cm up the front wall of the vagina. This mass of nerve tissue can't be felt unless it's stimulated, whether that's by a finger, a penis or a sex toy. But many women say that the G-spot doesn't exist. Others swear that it does, and have the orgasms – and sometimes female ejaculation – to prove it.

Gentlemen: the joy of the joystick

Yeah yeah, so you know your own penis better than you know the back of your hand. But the pleasure is in the details – and inch-by-inch knowledge of your penis's pleasure zones can make the difference between a good sex-toy experience and a mind-blowing one.

Men's bodies are actually packed with far more erogenous zones than the one that gets all the attention. You'll find that sex toys applied to different parts of the penis can work wonders in different ways.

Head

The smooth, curved tip of the penis is also known as the glans and is the most nerve-packed area of the male body. Use vibes on a low setting here, as sometimes it can be a bit too sensitive.

The shaft

This is the stalk of the penis. The skin here is very thin and sensitive and is packed with nerve endings.

Foreskin

The head of an uncircumcised penis is covered in a layer of loose skin called the foreskin, which wrinkles up when the penis is flaccid. When the old chap is standing to attention the foreskin peels back to expose the glans. Circumcision is the surgical removal of the foreskin, and is usually

performed for religious or hygiene reasons – some say that a circumcised penis is cleaner and more sensitive, while others argue that a penis that is protected by a foreskin is extra-responsive. Either way, there are plenty of happy penises both with and without foreskins.

Frenulum

The foreskin is attached to the head by a tiny triangle of super-sensitive skin called the frenulum. It's so sensitive that the tiniest lick, nibble or buzz from a vibe can tip a man over the edge into orgasm.

Testicles

Designed to manufacture sperm and the male sex hormone testosterone, the testicles hang loosely behind the penis in a little sack of skin called the scrotum. The line that runs down the scrotum between the balls, known as the raphe, is another highly erogenous zone.

The prostate gland

This is the backdoor entry to a world of wonderful orgasms. It is located a couple of centimetres up the front wall of the rectum. Often referred to as the male equivalent of the G-spot, or P-spot, the prostate gland is incredibly sensitive to pressure. Men can pass an enjoyable evening experimenting with anal vibrators, beads and butt plugs: many men say that prostate gland stimulation makes the difference between so-so sex and the kind that can make a grown man cry – with pleasure, of course.

Perineum

This hairless patch of skin between his balls and his anus is incredibly sensitive to stimulation – it's a way of accessing the prostate gland without going up the bum. A well-timed push here or a carefully placed sex toy can trigger an instant, intense, male orgasm.

Use your tongue to prise open his foreskin. Then give him a double-header: using lots of saliva, your tongue and a vibe work together to give him a wet, wobbly treat.

Different types of orgasm

Think there's only one type of orgasm? Think again.
There are as many variations on the theme of bed-rocking
climaxes are there are female bodies ... whatever rocks
your boat, there's a toy to get you there.

Clitoral
Most ladies need some clit stim to climax: in fact, it's the
most common and reliable way of reaching female orgasm.
You can stimulate the whole clitoris by using a flat, broad
vibrator that will send sexy sensations throughout the
whole vulva. Simply hold it against the clitoris, lie back
and think of England (and by that we mean David
Beckham stripped and steaming in the shower ...).

G-spot
Female orgasms without clit stim are often attributed to
the G-spot. If you're not sure where you stand on the G-spot
debate (see page 11), it can't do any harm to look for it!
Use a vibrator on your clitoris first, as you can't find the
G-spot unless you're already turned on. Then use a vibrator
with a curved tip, like a beckoning finger, designed to locate
and stimulate the G-spot. If you like more motor from your
toys, insert the Rabbit Pearl vibrator: the tiny whirring
balls are ergonomically designed to caress your G-spot.

Vaginal/Cervical orgasm

This kind of orgasm is about stimulating the inside of the vaginal walls right up to the cervix. While clitoral orgasms radiate sensations from the clitoris, women who come this way report feeling contractions that affect the whole pelvic region, forcing the back to arch (and the toes to curl).

Deep penetration is essential. First, choose the right toy: a long, broad dick-shaped dildo (as opposed to small, novelty clit stims). Then choose the right position, which means inserting the toy from behind, doggy-style, or bearing down on the toy from on top, so that she can push down to achieve the deep penetration she needs.

Nipple orgasm

They're more common than you might think: one study found that 29 per cent of women can reach orgasm from stimulation alone. Caress with a low-level vibrator to engorge the breasts. Then use a toy-tongue combo to finish what you've started, using flavoured nipple drops to sweeten the experience for both partners.

Anal orgasm

Direct anal stimulation has been shown to produce an orgasm in a minority of women, but all women can benefit from a little anal stimulation during intercourse, as the anal muscles contract during orgasm – having a toy up the butt can intensify these sensations beyond imagination.

Blended

This orgasm comes from having more than one primary area stimulated at once: the more nerve endings are stimulated, the more intense the resulting orgasm will be. The best combination is simultaneous clit and G-spot stimulation: for sheer convenience you can't beat the Rabbit, which is ergonomically designed to deliver pleasure to both these highly charged zones at once. Other sure-fire combinations to try are clitoris and nipples, or clitoris and ass. If you're feeling extremely adventurous, try the clitoral, vaginal and anal triple whammy, by inserting an anal vibe or love beads into the ass while using a Rabbit.

To tease and please her, slide the vibe inside her vagina and let her enjoy the full-up sensation for a few seconds. Then pull it almost, but not quite, out again. This stimulates the most sensitive part of her vagina (the first two inches) and promises, but doesn't yet deliver, a bed-rocking orgasm – delicious psychological torture.

Vibes for first-timers

Using a sex toy is a great way to open your eyes to all kinds of orgasmic possibilities. Men masturbate twice a day from their teens until old age. Women have to search to find their clitoris and vagina, so it's usual to need a little guidance.

The good news is that while it takes an average of 20 minutes for women to reach orgasm via oral sex, masturbation or penetration, using a vibrator can make you come in anything from 60 seconds to three minutes – less than the ad break in your favourite TV show, and much healthier than a cup of coffee and a biscuit.

Getting to know your body

Have a look at your genitals using a mirror: trace the sex toy over your vulva, your inner thighs, and gradually work your way towards your clitoris. Tickle and tease every inch of skin. Use your fingers as well as your toy to explore.

Once you've hit a spot that feels good, breathe deeply and stay with it. While some women come in seconds flat, others take three or four attempts before climaxing. Try to vary the sex toys and the positions you use, and every now and then try to reach orgasm through oral sex or masturbation (your own hand or your lover's). This book is packed full of enough ideas to keep even a seasoned sex-toy user happy for years.

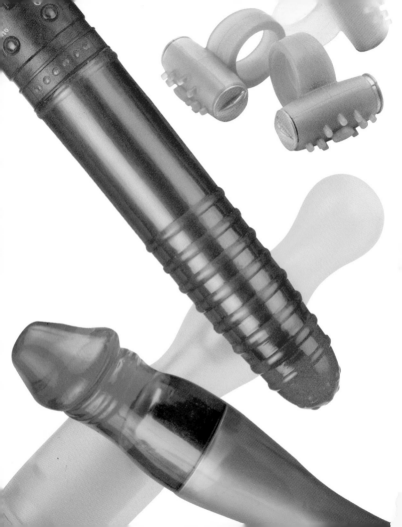

Kid in a candy store: choosing the right toy

I say 'kid in a candy store' because with the extensive range of sex toys on the market today, you'll be spoilt for choice and it's often hard to know where to begin. You need to take a few things into consideration: the material it's made from, how much it costs, the erogenous zones it's designed to stimulate, whether it lends itself to couple sex or not.

The right stuff

Not all sex toys are created equal: there are a wide range of different materials to choose from, all of which have their pros and cons. Read on to find out which suits your wallet, preferences and lifestyle.

Jelly and latex toys

These are cheap and cheerful, and usually come in bright, funky colours. They are porous, so can absorb lubricant, whether natural or artificial: work extra hard to keep it clean. If you're allergic to condoms, you'll know about it. Hold it against your inner thigh before putting it inside. Both jelly and latex toys should be used with water-based lubes as, being porous, they can absorb other kinds of lubricant, making a haven for all sorts of bacteria you want to avoid introducing to your genitals. (For more on lubricants, see page 62.)

Silicone toys

Mid-price range, this flexible substance bends to your body's curves and warms up quickly. It's also relatively long lasting. Caveat: you CANNOT use silicone-based lubricants with silicone toys, as the lubricant breaks down the toy.

Realistic

The newest and most expensive of the bunch, the most popular realistic finish is called Cyberskin, so called because it's as near to the real thing as you can get. This material is warm to the touch, feeling more sensual; toys tend to be replicas of genitalia, so you're talking lifelike penises and vaginas – which will either turn you on or freak you out. They must be stored in cool, dry conditions or they're vulnerable to mould.

Plastic and acrylic

Smooth and hard to the touch, these are easy to clean and totally non-porous, which means you can use any kind of lubrication. However, they're inflexible and can be really cold, the shock of which can interrupt your pleasure. They can also be noisy, and the acrylic kind are flammable: no smoking in bed with these around!

Even better than the real thing: lifelike toys vs. plastic fantastic

While some sex toys are so eerily like the real thing, you'd be forgiven for worrying they might wee all over the toilet seat, others are so unlike traditional sex toys that only those in the know would ever guess that that little lipstick/glittery rubber butterfly/innocent-looking little pebble is actually a sex toy. There are pros and cons to these toys: the funky, unrealistic toys are less embarrassing, say, when you're going through the scanner at the airport. However, the realistic variety – whether penis or vagina – are great if you're fantasising about someone in particular. They can also add a thrilling dimension if you trail the 'penis' all over your skin, lips, nipples and buttocks as foreplay for yourself.

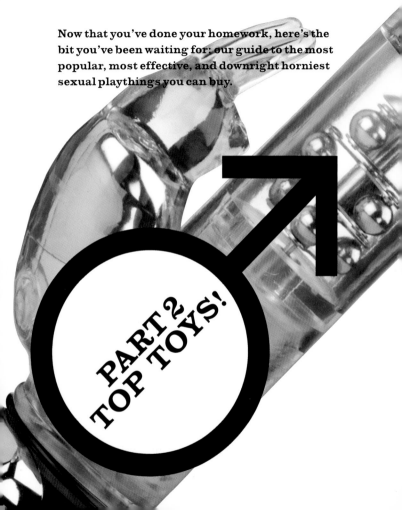

Now that you've done your homework, here's the bit you've been waiting for: our guide to the most popular, most effective, and downright horniest sexual playthings you can buy.

PART 2
TOP TOYS!

All the toys you'll ever need!

Stimulating the clitoris is the most popular, fastest and easiest way for a woman to reach orgasm, and that's where vibrators come into their own. Although they come in dozens of shapes and sizes, some barely bigger than your finger and designed for direct clitoral stimulation, and other, larger models made for penetration, all of them have one thing in common: they're the orgasmic equivalent of gunpowder, so get ready for fireworks!

Shafted!

Shaft vibes – fake penises that have a little whirring motor inside – deliver the best of both worlds. They provide the vibrations that are needed to stimulate the clitoris, but they're also large enough for satisfactory penetration, and to make them into a dildo, all you need to do is switch it off! Because of their versatility, they're ideal sex toys for first-timers or the chronically indecisive.

They come in all shapes, sizes and textures: some are smooth and lifelike, others have ridges around the base to stimulate the vaginal opening. Shaft vibes can be made from almost any material, but jelly, latex or silicone are ideal because they feel warm and flexible during penetration, and the soft tip is ideal for clitoral action.

Where does it go?

Wherever you like! That's the beauty of shaft vibes. However, if you're thinking of going up the butt, it's a good idea to get a vibe specifically designed for this location (see anal vibes, page 58).

Solo

Combine the satisfaction of penetration with the stimulation of the clit buzz: hold it against the clit for 10 seconds, then place it inside you for another 20, give the clit another 10 seconds' pleasure, and repeat it until your climax overwhelms you. By varying the pressure and pleasure in this way, you can delay your orgasm by up to five minutes, meaning that the eruption, when it comes, will be more powerful than ever.

Together

The ultimate in foreplay for lazy guys and girls, shaft vibes take the work out of turning each other on. He can hold it against her clitoris to get her wet, ready and willing to host his cock: she can trace the vibe along his balls and inner thighs to get the blood flowing to his pelvic region and strengthen his erection.

Sextra

Invest in a shaft vibe with a gently curved tip and try to find your G-spot. These gently bent vibes act like a beckoning

She takes his balls in her mouth and holds the vibe underneath her chin – an amazing sensation for him, while the toy does all the work for her.

finger, caressing the front of your vaginal wall, arousing your G-spot and making orgasm much more likely than mere thrusting and clit stim.

Mini-vibes and clitoral stimulators

More women come from clitoral stimulation than anything else – 80 per cent as opposed to 20 per cent from penetration. A clit stim could totally change the way you masturbate. Most clit stims are small and can fit in your handbag – some are even disguised as lipsticks or mobile phones.

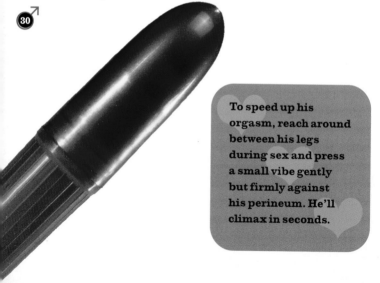

To speed up his orgasm, reach around between his legs during sex and press a small vibe gently but firmly against his perineum. He'll climax in seconds.

Where does it go?

They're designed to be held against the clitoris, but can be traced all over the body. These toys come into their own by paying attention to places where other, clunkier vibes can't reach. Vaginal penetration is best left to the big boys.

Solo

Every woman has micro-erogenous zones: if directly on the clitoris feels a bit overpowering, try just to the side of or above the clitoral hood. You'll find that changing the position of the vibe by a millimetre to the left or right could work for you – try to find your own individual hot spot.

Together

Mini-vibes lend themselves to standing-up sex: he stands behind her and she's pressed against a wall, with the mini-vibe held fast between the wall and her clitoris. She's sandwiched between her lover and her toy – delicious! This position is also recommended for experimenting with fantasies of abduction and control.

Sextra

Place the mini-vibe in your mouth or against your cheek before giving oral sex (although take care not to dribble all over the battery bit). The humming sensation as you blow, lick and suck can be absolutely mind-blowing (as well as lightening the workload for the person giving the oral sex).

The Rabbit

This is the Rolls Royce of sex toys. The shaft of the vibrator is filled with tiny internal balls which rotate at the flick of a switch to stimulate the inside of the vaginal wall and the G-spot. In addition, there are two little vibrating 'ears' (hence the Rabbit tag) which stimulate the clitoris. Because it's a multi-tasking machine, the controls can sometimes look a bit like the flight deck of a spaceship: but this simply means that you can experiment with different combinations of hard and soft, fast and slow. Perhaps you like fast stimulation on the clitoris, but prefer to have the internal balls rotating at a lower level, or even turned off altogether. Or maybe you love intense stimulation internally on the G-spot with low or no clit stim.

Where does it go?

The central shaft is designed to penetrate the vagina, while the 'ears' caress either side of the clitoris. You don't need to insert the Rabbit to feel its benefits; orgasm is easily reached by holding the ears against the clitoris.

Solo

Why not insert it and look at yourself in a mirror? Most of us never get to see our 'orgasm' face – but you're virtually guaranteed to climax this way, so why not check it out.

Together

Can you handle a totally sextreme sexperience? Then aim for double penetration. She inserts the vibe, and while she enjoys clitoral and vaginal stimulation, he enters her from behind. It's quite advanced and a little bit porn-star, but worth it if you don't take it too seriously: women who have sex this way say they've never felt more 'full up', while the vibes from the toy will send shock waves throughout his entire pelvic region, too.

Sextra

The efficient clitoral stimulation means the Rabbit is ideal for a warm-up before quickie sex: placing the ears against your clitoris for a few seconds to jump-start your body's arousal cycle and you'll start to lubricate, ready for a penis.

Look, Mum, no hands!

Hands-free vibes range from strap-on clit stims to mini-bullet vibes encased in a pair of knickers that operate by remote control. They're often fun shapes, usually soft plastic, and the power pack and controls are either remote control or connected to the vibe via a long wire, meaning you can move around. They're designed for clitoral stimulation but you can combine with a dildo for penetration. The remote control is ideal if you want to let your partner control your pleasure; just hand over the control unit, lie back and abandon yourself to the pleasure – or teasing.

Where does it go?

The vibe rests against the clitoris. It can also be strapped onto a man and rests under his balls to make intercourse, masturbation or oral sex go with an extra buzz.

Solo

Your hands aren't busy clamping the vibe against your clit, so put them to good use: read your favourite erotic book or call your partner for phone sex.

Together

This is great for woman-on-top sex, because he gets the visual treat of seeing her body, and both partners have their hands free to stimulate breasts, thighs, anus and other erogenous zones you can't pamper when your hands are full.

Sextra

Some advanced remote-control knickers can be worn under clothes, so are a great way to spice up an otherwise ordinary night out and to experiment with fantasies of control and domination. Will she be able to keep a straight face while she comes?

She wears her favourite sheer panties and he holds the vibrator against her clit: he times how long she can handle the stimulation before she's begging to have him inside her. For extra urgency, she keeps the panties on and he pulls them to one side and penetrates her.

Inside story

The best toys designed for penetration …

Dildos

These are the simplest (and oldest) kind of sex toy – crudely put, they're penis-shaped toys that don't vibrate, designed for penetrating the vagina and/or anus. They come in all shapes and sizes, from huge, realistic, flesh-coloured dicks complete with veins to glittery, bendy, brightly coloured ones. Some are smooth and straight while others are gently curved at the end for a greater chance of stimulating your G-spot. Ridged and knobbly textured ones can provide extra stimulation, although you might need a bit of extra lube to cope with them.

Where does it go?

Inside the vagina. Large dildos are often bigger than the average penis, so you might need a bit of lubrication if you're using it on your own.

Solo

They're great if you get off on thrusting during intercourse, and they can also let you experiment with what kind of speed/depth of penetration works for you without your boyfriend asking, 'Is that OK?' or getting tired. Invest in a dildo with a suction base, attach to the wall or bed and practise lowering yourself onto it slowly, noticing which areas of your vagina are the most sensitive.

39
↓

Together

For a real visual treat and a physical treat for her, he can put a dildo in her while giving her analingus/rimming (using his tongue on her anus), or using his tongue to stimulate the clitoris.

Sextra

Use a small vibrator to trace your nipples and other erogenous zones while you've got the larger one inside you. If you're used to climaxing without anything inside, you'll be pleasantly surprised by the full-up feeling you get when your vaginal walls contract around the dildo as you orgasm.

Strap-on dildo

This is a specially made dildo that comes with its own harness, which straps on rather like a thong. It has all the advantages of a dildo but penetration can be harder and faster with the weight of a partner behind it, and the receiver surrenders the element of control, which can be very thrilling. Lesbian couples have used them for years to experience a feeling of penetration and dominance during sex and to have 'intercourse'. More recently, hetero couples have been experimenting with strap-ons: they're great to use in relationships where the man is having trouble maintaining an erection, and many open-minded (and open-bottomed!) men enjoy the feeling of being penetrated by their female partner. The harnesses available have either one or two straps and are made of nylon or leather. A single strap allows your partner easy access to your genitals for manual stimulation when you are wearing the harness. Not all dildos are harness-compatible, so it's best to buy a strap-on kit – that is, a harness and dildo in one.

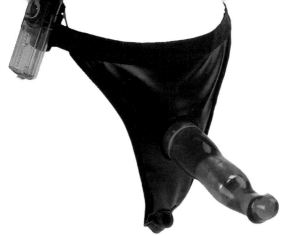

Solo

This is a great way for girls to fantasise about what it's like to have a penis: why not double the pleasure with a hands-free vibe and a strap-on dildo: enjoy the feeling of the buzz on your clitoris while you 'masturbate' your penis and get lost in horny fantasy.

Together

During girl-on-girl sex, this can be a great way to experience the good old-fashioned missionary position: the partner wearing the strap-on climbs on top of her lover and slides the dildo into her vagina. The feeling of breasts and clits grinding against each other while one partner is penetrated means it's a completely different experience from the humdrum hetero version.

Sextra

Trussing up your lover and strapping into her harness can be an incredibly erotic experience – and, with a couple of extra-sharp tugs on the straps, you can incorporate a little mild pain and experiment with bondage, too.

Double dildo

These usually non-vibrating toys are bestsellers among homo and hetero couples alike. Some consist of a base with two lifelike fake penises attached, while others are long, slim, curved dildos with two 'heads'.

Where does it go?

Designed for vaginal penetration, although with a little bit of patience and a whole lotta lube, can be used anally, too.

Solo

It might be a toy for two, but a double dildo can fuel fantasies while you're masturbating. While one head of the dildo is inside you, caress the other one, imagining you're giving your fantasy lover a hand-job, or that the 'penis' is an extension of your own body and you're about to penetrate someone else.

Together

During girl-on-girl sex, foreplay followed by slowly lowering yourselves down onto the dildo at the same time is a tried-and-tested treat. Continue to play with clits and tits and enjoy the feeling of bringing each other to orgasm whilst being penetrated by the toy.

Sextra

Get lippy: one partner is penetrated with the dildo while the other takes it in her mouth and simulates oral sex.

Love eggs/Ben Wa balls

They might look like Christmas tree decorations, but these shiny round baubles are not for display. Because most of them have no batteries (although buzzy variations are available), they're the ultimate in portable play. Once the balls are placed inside the vagina, the vaginal walls automatically grip them. This trains your internal muscles to grip hard, meaning your orgasms will become stronger and your partner's penis will feel snugger inside you during vaginal intercourse. They vary from chrome ones with bells inside to plastic ones with bobbles on to stimulate every nerve ending in the vaginal wall.

Where do they go?

They're placed inside the vagina, rather like a tampon. The more you move about, the more stimulated you'll be.

Solo

While many sex toys can only be used during a masturbation session, the pleasure that love balls bring can last for hours: insert them when you're pottering about the house and enjoy the way the vibrations from the vacuum cleaner buzz your insides!

Together

If she's into anal sex, doing it doggy-style while her love balls fill her up from the inside can be particularly satisfying – especially if she, or her partner, whips them out or gently rotates them during penetration.

Sextra

To turn your love eggs from a solo treat into a thrill for two, ask your lover to insert them gently into you.

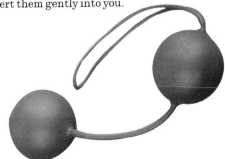

Boys' toys

Boys just wanna have fun, too: why should women get all the best sex toys? Recent advances in technology mean that men-only playthings have never been so much fun.

Cock rings – non-vibrating

Got wood? Well, a cock ring can help you stay that way. Cock rings work by stopping blood from draining back out of the erect penis, so it stays hard because it's engorged with blood. This can be useful for maintaining an erection if you suffer from premature ejaculation, to prolong masturbation until you can't bear to hold off the climax any more (we all know that there's nothing as satisfying as delayed gratification and that the orgasm, when it finally comes, will be even more intense).

They can be made from stretchy rubber or metal, silicone or leather, hard or soft. They can be smooth, spiked, and any colour you care to mention. Some men find wearing cock rings makes the erection firmer, a result that can make both partners happy.

If you've never used one before, your best bet is an adjustable and/or flexible c-ring. This way, you get to try a few different levels of tight and loose to decide which one you're most comfortable with. Hard, inflexible rings are impossible to remove until your erection goes down.

Where does it go?

C-rings are designed to fit around the base of the penis and the scrotum, restricting flow out of the penis. This stops the balls rising up into the body, which happens at the point of orgasm, so stops the orgasm until you remove the ring.

CAVEAT! Because you're talking about stopping blood flow, there are some ground rules. Never wear it for longer than 20 minutes, and take it off right away if it starts to hurt. Anyone with a history of circulatory problems, diabetes, nerve disorders, blood clots, or anyone who's on blood-thinning medication should not use a cock ring.

Solo

Put on your cock ring before you're erect, and enjoy the unusual feeling of tightness as you get hard.

47
↓

Together

Having sex from behind is delicious but fraught with problems: men often find the sensation so overwhelming that they come too quickly, while women get frustrated because he hasn't allowed long enough to caress her G-spot as much as she needs to achieve orgasm. Slipping on a cock ring can delay his pleasure, and so increase hers.

Take it further:
If you want a more intense sensation, try putting one flexible ring around the base of your penis and another around and underneath the testicles.

Cock rings – vibrating

They're usually made of soft silicone, either smooth or ridged, with a little vibrator attached, and come in a variety of funky colours and shapes, the most popular being a little blue dolphin-shaped vibe. Because they're so small, the batteries and control are usually attached with a wire. He can masturbate with it on; but where these really come into their own – and what they were designed for – is partner sex. A bullet vibrator attached to the cock ring is positioned so that it will run up against the women's clitoris during intercourse while also vibrating his penis. This is great for women who need more stimulation during penetration. It also means that your hands are free to explore each other's bodies rather than having to hold a sex toy near the genitals. It can make all the difference for the 50 per cent of women who find it hard to reach orgasm through vaginal penetration alone. It effectively turns his penis into a vibrator that's inside her.

Where does it go?

They vary: some will fit around the base of the penis, others will slip under the testicles, too. If you're planning to use this toy during intercourse, you'll need to make sure the vibrator nestles against her clitoris.

Solo

For a different kind of buzz, you can flip this toy upside down so the vibrator is underneath the penis and facing inward. This stimulates the balls during intercourse or masturbation.

49 ↓

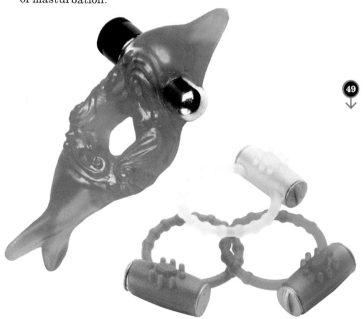

Together

Lord knows that most couples adore missionary, but it doesn't always hit the spot – a vibrating c-ring gets maximum results with minimum effort from both partners. It makes simultaneous orgasms more likely as well: speeding up her climax and slowing down his.

Sextra tip

Top tip! Trim the hair around the base of the penis before using any cock ring – now's not the time for a guy to find out what a bikini wax feels like.

Sleeves – non-vibrating

Sleeves are toys that re-create the feel of inserting a penis into a vagina. Cyberskin has the look and feel of real skin. Comfort and snugness is the key and this can usually be achieved by adding lots of lubricant. Finding a sleeve that is snug yet elastic enough for easy removal is important, as is choosing a material that is easy to keep clean.

Where does it go?

Softer toys can be great to put a semi-erect penis into, and to enjoy the gradual 'cuddle' the sleeve gives your penis as your erection gets harder and harder.

Solo
If you're flying solo, try it hands free, clamped between furniture or wedged into a doorframe.

Together
If he loves to watch her masturbate but also loves the feel of a sleeve, he can use it while she plays with herself in front of him: the ultimate in visual and physical stimulation.

Take it further
For couples, this really comes into its own when a woman isn't comfortable with sex, e.g. after childbirth. She can clamp it between her legs and it's the second best thing for achieving the closeness without the vaginal penetration.

Sleeves – vibrating
Vibrating sleeves tend to be less realistic than the non-vibe kind, but offer stronger stimulation for men. They're usually made of jelly or silicone and can be smooth, but more often have ridges or knobbles inside for extra stimulation. They usually stretch to accommodate all shapes and sizes of penis. Use more lube than you think you'll need: the latex/silicone will tear at your skin and it will become VERY uncomfortable.

Where does it go?
Fits snugly over the penis. You need a full erection before you put on this toy as it's designed to be a snug fit. You can thrust in and out, or move it up and down over your penis.

Solo
Adding a little warm water to your lube will give your willy an even warmer welcome into this sex toy.

Together
Ever heard of 'queening'? This popular BDSM game involves the man lying back while the woman straddles his shoulders and lowers herself down onto his face. It's an intense buzz for both partners, but if he wants to leave one hand free to stimulate her clitoris or anus, he can use a vibrating sleeve so that his own orgasm is taken care of.

Sextra

Although most men who aren't used to sex toys find that they come within seconds the first time they use a vibe sleeve, they can actually be good for training yourself to come a bit slower. Experiment by turning up the speed and then stopping stimulation dead just before you pass the 'point of no return'. It should mean that you eventually stop spunking in your pants like a teenager.

Penis sleeves were designed with the whole body of the penis in mind. She can make it interesting by clamping the sleeve between her legs and letting him penetrate the sleeve from behind: this is great for guys who love rear-entry sex and girls who find it uncomfortable.

Every home has a built-in sex toy: the shower head. A jet of warm (but not hot) water on her clitoris or his perineum can make you climax faster than you can say 'slippery when wet …'

Backdoor lovin'

Toys designed to stimulate the anus for boys and girls.

BUTT SERIOUSLY: READ THIS BEFORE YOU BEGIN
Anal sex toys have their own special rules when it comes to health and safety:

Golden Rule One: Clean up your act. Bacteria that live in the anus are particularly threatening if they find their way into a mouth, vagina, clitoris, penis or any open wounds. Follow the cleaning instructions properly and do use a condom. Never transfer a vibe from the anus to the vagina, clitoris, penis or mouth without washing it first, or putting a new condom on it.

Golden Rule Two: Lubrication, lubrication, lubrication. Unlike the vagina, the anus doesn't produce its own natural lubrication (no matter how horny you get!). So it's vital to use plenty of appropriate joy juice to make the course of true love run smooth. Failing to use the right lube could result in tears in the delicate skin of the rectum. Ouch. For more information on lubes, see page 62.

Golden Rule Three: Never put anything up your ass that doesn't have a flared base: sex toys for the anus are shaped this way for a reason, to stop them disappearing altogether: easier than you'd think when hands and bottoms are lubed up and passions are running high.

Anal beads aka love beads:

They may look like a kiddie's toy, but they're anything but. Love beads are a series of marble-sized beads made of hard plastic strung together on a cord with a loop at one end. They feel good when inserted into the anus one at a time. Because they're small and easy to use, beads are great for people who are new to anal play. The smallest strings only comprise one or two beads and often come in cute candy colours. Before use, run your fingers up and down to check there are no sharp and potentially dangerous snags.

Where it goes:

In the anus. When you use your beads – either alone or with a partner – always apply plenty of lube. Slowly insert them, one at a time and remove them as you approach your climax. Men, in particular, who have an orgasm this way report total loss of control.

Solo

Find out whether fast or slow works best for you: as you approach climax, either tease yourself and build up to a rippling orgasm by removing them slooooowly. The next time, whip them out at the last minute to trigger an orgasm that could be more intense than any you've had before.

Together

If you're having vaginal sex, love beads lend themselves to the doggy position: she kneels on all fours, while he enters her from behind and thrusts, gently pulling on the beads so that she's completely overwhelmed by the sensations.

Sextra

Once the beads are inside you, rotate them very gently and very slowly, or ask your partner to do it for you, so that every inch of your rectum is stimulated.

Butt plugs

While a dildo will give a nice, 'full' feeling of penetration, a butt plug is designed so that the prostate gland will be stimulated, but still allow you a degree of flexibility. If you want to leave the toy in while you have penetrative sex yourself/make a phone call/whatever, then get a butt plug.

As with dildos, you can find rubber and plastic anal toys, but silicone makes the very best material for an anal toy because it is so easy to clean. Size is a matter of personal preference, but if you're new to anal play you might want to start with a finger-width toy (or, indeed, a finger, if you want to check whether you like it or not).

Although women don't have a prostate gland, many enjoy using butt plugs, especially the 'ponygirl', a plug with a little horsehair tail that's great for kitsch appeal.

Where it goes:

Does what it says on the tin – this slips into the anus. Before you insert it, use a clean finger to insert some lube into your anus and relax and warm up the muscles. Wash your hands then, before inserting the butt plug. Work it around in a circular motion as it slides in.

Solo

For orgasm overload, assume a kneeling position and masturbate with your favourite hands-free vibe/sleeve while using your free hand to gently, slowly rotate the butt plug in your ass.

Together

Men find that wearing a butt plug during penetrative sex can trigger the most intense orgasms ever as the prostate gland is stimulated from within as well as without.

Take it further

Wear a butt plug in anticipation of a hot sex session – and let your partner discover it as he/she works her way down your body during foreplay!

Anal vibes

These super-slim vibrators are designed especially for the back passage. They can be used for anything from a sensation of fullness to stimulating the prostate gland during intercourse, and send waves of pleasure through your whole pelvic region. They also have the added benefit of loosening up the sphincter, making penetration with a penis, hand or larger sex toy much easier.

They're better for anal play than vaginal vibes, which are designed to stimulate the clitoris and G-spot. They're available in all different kinds of materials, but the flexibility of silicone or jelly vibes means that beginners should try the softer, bendier kind to experiment.

Where it goes:

Although they will feel perfectly at home in an anus, they're small enough to go pretty much anywhere you care to put them. Build delicious tension prior to inserting in the anus by trailing it all over your (or your partner's) most sensitive erogenous zones.

Solo

Experiment with a variety of different positions. Some guys find it easier to find the G-spot while lying on their back, legs in the air: others prefer to bend over doggy-style, or lie on their fronts. Why not try all the positions in one night

and rate them in a top ten so your partner knows what you want from a bumming session in future?

Together
Hetero sex: spice up missionary sex by slipping a vibe up his ass and watching his body melt.

Sextra
Try using the anal vibe all over your partner's body before sticking it where the sun don't shine: it'll wake up the nerve endings in glorious anticipation of what's to come.

Care of your sex toy

Because your sex toy is going to spend its life where the sun don't shine, it's vital you keep it clean. If left unwashed between uses, bacteria can build up. Unkempt sex toys will become smelly and, at worst, they can become mouldy and a source of nasty infections. Don't say we didn't warn you.

Even though you clean your sex toy after every use, give it a quick wipe-down before each playtime in order to make extra sure it's as clean as you want it to be.

If you do leave it on the draining board to dry, it might be an idea to put it away before Granny comes round for afternoon tea.

Safe sex: toys need protection too

Apply the same rules as you would to oral, manual or penetrative sex. If you're not sure your dildo or vibrator is perfectly clean, put a condom on it. And if you're sharing sex toys, always cover with a condom and put on a new one between sessions.

Storing your toy

The knicker drawer is the traditional hiding place for your battery-powered best friend, but it's worth investing in a specialist carrying case. These are available from sex shops and are cunningly disguised as funky washbags or cosmetic purses.

Love potion number nine: fun with oils, lubes and potions

To lube or not to lube? There is no question! Using a purpose-made lubricant with your sex toys has endless benefits. When she becomes aroused, a woman's natural juices automatically make penetration easier. But for some reason she might dry up a bit; maybe she's a little dehydrated or nervous. And some girls simply don't get as wet as others do.

But sometimes you want to go on playing for longer than your natural lubrication lasts. Toy materials can absorb the lube quicker than a penis, so it's especially important to use extra lube when playing with your favourite vibe or dildo. And, of course, the anus doesn't make any natural lubrication at all, so it's vital to use shop-bought lube when using anal toys.

There are a gazillion different kinds of lubricant, from tried-and-tested water-based juices to cutting-edge silicone formulations. Which one you use depends on whether you're playing solo or with a partner. It even has to be compatible with your sex toys and any condoms you might be using, and of course it's also a matter of personal taste. Whatever kind you use, keep some tissues, vibe wipes or wet wipes handy in case of excess spillage – you're bound to get carried away.

Play adults only hide-and-seek. Turn on your vibe and hide it somewhere around the house – under a sofa cushion, in the kitchen drawer, a tree in the garden – anywhere you'd like to have sex. Time how long your partner takes to find the vibe: he then owes you that many minutes of toy time.

Water-based lubes like KY jelly are non-sticky and they don't affect some of the hi-tech material that the sex toys are made of. Oil-based lubricants last longer and feel nice and slippery, but must be used with care as they can break down condoms within 60 seconds. Most of the 'make-do' lubricants that people use when they've run out of the shop-bought stuff, including petroleum jelly, hair conditioner, sun lotion or cooking fat, contain or are made from oil. Go easy with these. Many of them contain harsh perfumes and chemicals that aren't designed to go anywhere near your genitals! Silicone lubes last for as long as you can keep going (they're actually based on the lubricant NASA use to keep their spaceships moving smoothly). They shouldn't break down condoms, but they will ruin silicone and cyberskin toys. Because silicone lubes can be very thick in consistency, they're great for anal play, which can be rougher and tougher than other kinds.

Smell me, taste me

Flavoured and perfumed lubes are great fun, especially if oral sex is a big part of your sex play. They're available in a wide range of flavours, from chocolate to fruit. They're designed to be used all over the body, licked off nipples and massaged into inner thighs, as well as for penetrative use. Some of them are only for novelty use, so check your flavoured lube is suitable for internal use before going inside and, I can't say it enough, latex-compatible.

The new kids on the lube block are self-heating formulations that contain ingredients that bring about a warm, tingly feeling, stimulating blood flow to the genitals when they come into contact with water, saliva or natural lubrication (add water yourself if you're not naturally wet). If you're planning to use self-heating lubes, try a 'patch test' first – apply a tiny amount to your genitals 24 hours or so before you plan to use the lube with your partner. If there's any inflammation, stick to a plain, water-based lube.

Genital balms have the same effect, but are designed to stimulate rather than to lubricate. Pussy rub and cock rub work by gently increasing blood flow to the genitals, giving nature a helping hand by simulating the conditions that naturally happen when you're horny. They are often flavoured with mint or cinnamon to add to the tingly sensations, and make oral sex even more enticing. Just make sure they're condom-compatible: check each one individually and, again, try a patch test before going the whole hog. These creams mimic your natural state of arousal, fooling the body into thinking it's party time. And if you're already aroused, these balms are the equivalent of lighting a firecracker under your orgasm.

And finally… warm your lube between your hands before applying it to a sex toy or your partner – ice-cold lube can cool down hot passions pretty quickly!

Got a filthy fantasy you can't say out loud? Using chocolate body paint, spell it out in mirror writing on your partner's body. Then place him in front of the mirror and ask him to read it out.

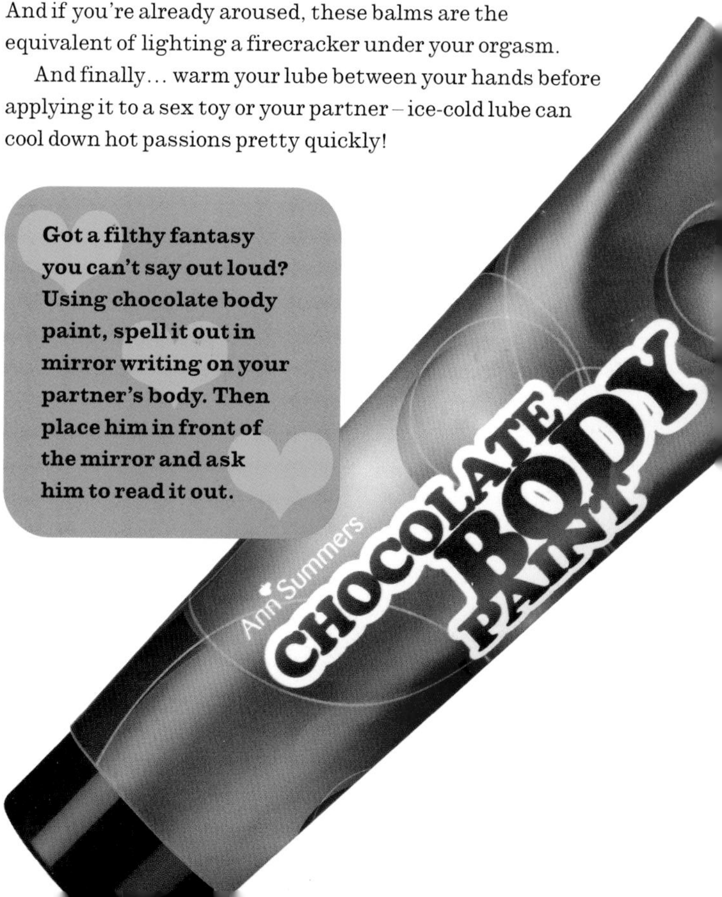

Ann Summers

CHOCOLATE BODY PAINT

PART 3
THE BEST
OF THE
REST

Sex toys don't stop at hi-tech gadgets designed to stimulate your genitals: there's a whole world of boudoir playthings that can work on the largest sex organ of all – your brain. Erotic power exchange – taking it in turns to be dominant and submissive in bed – is a great way for couples to experiment with sex play, and the good news is, you don't need much kit and caboodle to start exploring.

If she usually wears the trousers, she might love it if her man ties her to the bed with a pair of handcuffs before having his way with her. If he's usually the boss, he'll love it if she takes control, plays the dominatrix and spanks him. Everyone's different, so buy whichever toys appeal to you, mix it up, experiment … and play!

69

Tie me up, tie me down: bondage for beginners

A little gentle restraint during sex provides a physical and psychological thrill that's hard to beat. Whether you want to tie your partner up and dominate him/her – a position known as the 'top' – or you want to be strapped to the bed while you lie there and receive all the pleasure – the 'bottom' – there's a toy out there to help you.

Take it in turns to play top and bottom, and see which pairing works best for you.

Start by tying each other up with a pair of old stockings

– soft and with a little give in them. If you like the sensation it's well worth investing in custom-made, shop-bought bondage gear, as it's designed with comfort and safety in mind.

Bondage tape is made of PVC and is quick, easy, safe, re-usable and can be cut to length, so you can either use it to tie just the hands or bind an entire body.

Cuffs with Velcro ties come in bright, funky designs and can also be undone at a second's notice. Nylon bondage ropes are soft, supple and smooth so any knots should slide undone easily. Many rope kits come with complex, full-body tying-up instructions that take hours to perfect, but mastering the art can be a highly seductive process – or at least a good laugh. Why not give your sex play an extra dimension by assuming roles while you tie each other up? Kidnapper and heiress held to ransom, Roman dictator and slave girl, horny doctor and vulnerable-but-excited patient having a full physical examination …

RESTRAINING ORDERS …
READ THIS BEFORE YOU BEGIN!

Keep power exchange safe and sexy by following these golden rules:

Golden Rule One: Never tie anyone so tightly they can't move at all, and use knots that can be untied quickly. Never tie anything around your own or your partner's neck. Set yourselves a time limit of half an hour.

Golden Rule Two: Because power exchange is the only time when people say no and mean yes – for example, your 'slave girl' might tell her 'master' she can't bear to be tied up any more, when in fact she's loving every sexy second – agree on a 'safe' word: a random code word that really means 'stop'.

Wrap each other up in bondage tape and simultaneously 'undress' each other in a frenzy of ripping and stripping. Relish the tiny stings the tape makes on your skin. The first one to totally disrobe their partner gets a sex toy massage lasting five minutes.

Slap and tickle

Introducing a little light spanking into your sexual repertoire can rev up solo sex and intercourse alike. Sexual excitement increases your tolerance for pain, which is why spanking and whipping can feel especially good in the heat of passion. Punishment and reward lend themselves to a million 'punishment' fantasies, from schoolteacher and naughty student to mistress and slave.

Test the water before you commit to buying a toy. Experiment with a little light slapping with your hands during sex or masturbation to see if the tiny pain gets you going or turns you off. The range of spanking toys is enormous, ranging from light, feathery paddles to leather, studded whips.

Indulge in a little role play with handcuffs. The 'jailer' wears the key to the cuffs on a ribbon around his / her neck to slap and tickle the tied-up partner's neck, chest and face during sex.

HAPPY SLAPPING …
READ THIS BEFORE YOU BEGIN!

The line between pleasure and pain is a fine one. Get the balance right and stay safe with these golden rules:

Golden Rule One: Spank your own hand or thigh to get an idea of how powerful the toy is: that way, you'll know what your lover likes. Men tend to have thicker skin than women, whose nerve endings are closer to the surface, making them more susceptible to pain.

Golden Rule Two: Contrast sharp slaps with feathery strokes and lots of cuddles so that the pain play is underpinned with some softness and affection.

Golden Rule Three: This only works in relationships when trust and commitment are already established: it's foolish to go here with someone who you don't know well.

Golden Rule Four: Finally, make sure you spank on the buttocks and thighs: blows administered to the body can damage the organs and kidneys. Avoid the front of the body and never, never strike the face or head or eyes, and – even if you think you can take it – whips, paddles and crops should only ever be used to tease and stroke the genitals, never to strike them. Failure to obey this golden rule could put an end to your bedroom play for good!

Paddles

A great way to start is with a paddle, available in sex shops. Some people love their spanking equipment so much that the mere sound of a leather paddle on the back of a hand is enough to get them sexually aroused. Usually made of wood, leather or plastic, paddles are often double-sided, with a hard, leather side for smacking and soft suede or velvet for a contrasting sensation. They come in bright, funky colours and feel good traced over the body softly as well as delivering a harder smack.

Solo

If she's masturbating face down on the bed, she can reach around and smack herself on the ass. This gets the blood rushing to her pelvic region, making her even more sensitive.

Together

Gently smacking her ass in time with his thrusts during doggy-style sex can help both partners keep up the steady rhythm.

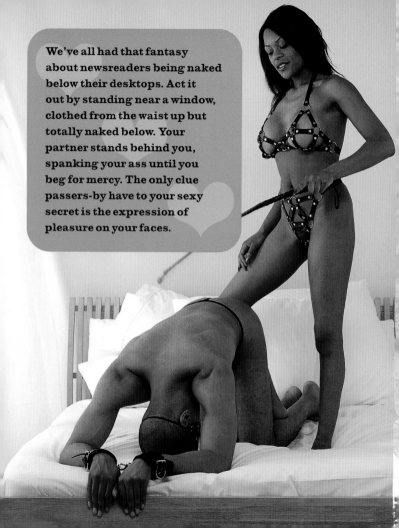

We've all had that fantasy about newsreaders being naked below their desktops. Act it out by standing near a window, clothed from the waist up but totally naked below. Your partner stands behind you, spanking your ass until you beg for mercy. The only clue passers-by have to your sexy secret is the expression of pleasure on your faces.

Riding crops

Made of leather or PVC, this is the halfway house between hands and paddles and hardcore whips and chains. They're great for providing a wide variety of sensations: some have feathers at the tip which can be traced all over the body and genitals before being used to deliver a short, sharp blow. They come in a variety of colours, from pretty pastels to black leather studded with crystals, and make a glamorous, sexy addition to any boudoir.

Solo

Experiment with rubbing the riding crop between your legs and using the tip of the crop to tease the clitoris, before using your favourite mini-vibe on yourself.

81 ↓

Together

A riding crop can double up as a restraint. During intercourse, the partner on top can raise their partner's hands above their head and then pin their hands to the bed using the crop. Disobedience will be punished by a lash from the whip!

Whips and chains

Whips and chains take you into hardcore BDSM territory and should only be used by those who already know they're comfortable with high levels of pain, because these things really can hurt! Stick to ones from sex shops as they're designed to give light pain, and avoid the real torture-chamber stuff. You can always try whipping fully clothed or through underwear if you want the power games but without the stinging sensations.

Solo

Whip yourself lightly on the back while masturbating for a delicious, stinging sensation that rivals the ripples of your orgasm.

Together

Play with the threat of the whip rather than using it to administer pain; the psychological thrill is often stronger than the physical sensation. Simply trail it over your lover's body, using the tip to tease nipples, buttocks, inner thighs and genitals.

Blindfolds

We have become so reliant on our sight for sexual arousal and stimulation that we forget how powerful the other senses can be. Take away your sight and you turn up all

your other senses – every taste, smell and touch will resonate even more. Breath on skin, words whispered into an ear, an ice cube or some candle wax trailed across skin … all these things feel more intense when they happen in the dark. Sensory deprivation can be taken one step further with an earplug and blindfold combo. As well as being erotic, many couples find that this experience really builds trust – after all, you're surrendering control and putting yourself at your lover's mercy …

Solo
Listen to an erotic podcast whilst wearing your blindfold. When you're not distracted by what you can see in front of you, your imagination goes into overdrive – and those sensations feel even more intense as a result.

Together
Blindfold your partner and then go to work on his/her body. Travel all over, kissing, licking, nibbling and caressing. Vary the speed and position of your movements; the idea is that, when the body doesn't know where the next move is coming from, the nerve endings are more receptive to every sensation.

Clamps

Nipple clamps look rather like large paperclips connected by a chain and work by applying pressure to the nipples, simulating a hard pinch. They can awaken sensitivity in men and women. They can be used solo to enhance masturbation or with a partner who will enjoy the visual treat of seeing a familiar pair of nipples or breasts trussed up and pinched. If you're new to this, go for adjustable clamps, so you can start with the lowest form of pressure and build up to the strongest pinch you can take. They start off with a gentle squeeze and build up to an excruciating tweak. Warning! Anything that deals with restricted blood flow should never be worn for longer than 20 minutes at a time. Those with blood disorders or diabetes should avoid nipple clamps completely (the same restrictions apply as to cock rings: see page 47).

Solo

Apply the clamps while masturbating in front of a mirror. Seeing the blood flow to your nipples can be hugely arousing and tip you over the edge into an intense orgasm.

Together

Apply the clamps during your favourite position, and ask your partner to tug on the chain between the clamps just as you approach orgasm.

Women feel pressured to reach orgasm as quickly as possible. Make the challenge to see how long she can handle the sex-toy pleasure before she climaxes. This reverse psychology works every time!

Food of love

It's said that the two great sensual pleasures in life are food and sex. So what better way to take sexuality to new heights than to combine the two? Sex shops are awash with great edible sex toys and flavoured massage oils and lubes that make foreplay even more mouthwatering and can pave the way for delicious orgasms. These toys are a bit messy, but they're a great prelude to fun, playful sex.

Eat me

You can now get edible panties, pouches and even bras made of rice paper, and decorated with sugar or finely spun jelly to melt on the tongue. It's best to soften them by licking gently at first, and make sure you don't bite your lover by accident! It's not the subtlest way to say you'd like some oral sex, but turning up in the bedroom clad in a pair of strawberry-flavoured knickers tends to get the message across. No hands are needed to remove these panties …

Solo

Get yourself in the mood for a masturbation marathon by wearing edible undies – and nothing else – around the house for a few hours.

A deux

Edible handcuffs can be a great low-risk (if high-calorie) way to attempt bondage. Imagine you're imprisoned and your lover is your hero – the dashing rescuer who has to lick, nibble, suck and eat your way to freedom!

Chocs away!

Chocolate body paint is perhaps the best known of edible sex toys, for a very good reason: chocolate contains a hormone called PEA or phenylethylamine, which stimulates a natural feel-good factor similar to the early stages of sexual arousal.

It's great to apply; why not write sexy suggestions all over your bodies or draw arrows pointing to the areas you'd like your partner to kiss or caress with a vibrator? Then you can lick it off with long, slow, sensual tongue strokes, and come up to give your partner a long, lingering, chocolatey kiss. Experiment with different sensations of hot and cold. A splash of cold body paint, straight from the fridge, will re-awaken jaded nerve endings, and a mouthful of hot chocolate on a cold day is a lovely warm treat.

Solo

Trace a little over your lips and lick and bite them while you're using your favourite vibrator. The tiny pain in your lips will make a delicious contrast to the vibes down below.

A deux

Give your lover's body a compliment: paint the areas you find sexiest, and as you're doing so tell him/her just why: 'I'm painting your neck now. I love the way you show your long neck when you throw your head back when you come.'

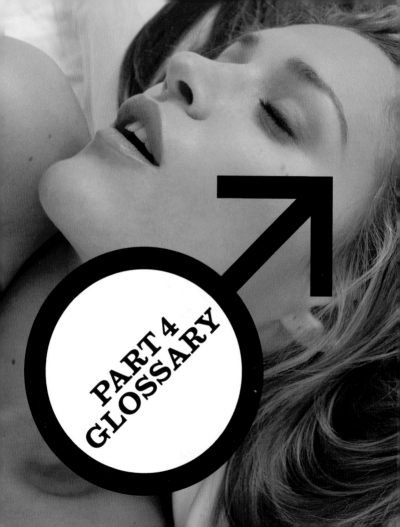

PART 4
GLOSSARY

Glossary of sex-toy language

Anal beads/love beads: A string of small plastic beads inserted into the anus, to stimulate the prostate gland.

Anal vibes: Small, slim vibrators designed to stimulate the anus. Often flared at the base so they don't disappear up the ass.

BDSM: A mixture of bondage and discipline, control and surrender, pleasure and pain: think tying up, spanking and role play.

Ben Wa balls: Small plastic or metal balls worn inside the vagina to stimulate and tone.

Bottom: The partner who surrenders control during BDSM play.

Blindfold: An easy way to indulge in a little bondage play; delicious surrender.

Butt plugs: Anal plugs are custom made to go up the ass and made of jelly or latex: the flared base means that unlike dildos they can't disappear up the rectum, so they're safer than using vibrators or dildos.

Clitoral Stimulators: Small vibrators designed specifically for direct use on the clitoris (as opposed to penetrative use).

Cock ring: This is a rubber or metal ring placed around the base of the penis to strengthen an erection and/or delay orgasm.

Plug in, baby: synchronise your MP3 players and listen to your favourite sexy songs while you're toying with each other, getting limbs and sex toys tangled up in the wires. This intensifies your love-making session, but also acts as a distraction, so it's great for delaying his orgasm if he sometimes comes a little too quickly.

Cyberskin: The next best thing to human skin; popular in realistic penis and vagina sex toys.

Dildo: A fake, solid penis in a variety of sizes and materials.

Double dildo: This model has two penis-like heads for use by two people.

Hands-free vibes: A vibrator with a remote control and battery pack.

Harness: A nylon or leather strap, worn around the pelvis, which holds a strap-on dildo in place.

Jelly: A rubbery, slightly sticky material used to make sex toys.

Love beads: See anal beads.

Love balls/love eggs: See Ben Wa balls.

Latex: A rubbery plastic used to make soft sex toys.

Lubricants: Lotions and potions applied to genitals and/or sex toys, making sex play slippery, comfortable and safe.

Nipple clamps: Pinching clips applied to the nipples and often attached with a chain.

Paddle: Wooden, plastic or leather toy for light spanking.

Restraints: Any device from ropes, tape or handcuffs used in bondage games.

Riding crop: A small whip used to slap and stimulate.

Silicone: The most luxurious material sex toys can be made from.

Strap-on: A dildo or butt plug attached to a harness for penetration.

Top: The person in control during BDSM play.

Vibrator: Does what it says on the tin! A toy that vibrates with varying speeds, and when it's applied to the clitoris is one of the most sure-fire ways for a woman to reach orgasm. The most popular and versatile kind of sex toy, can be used for penetration and anal stimulation too. (See Anal vibes.)

Whip: Leather or plastic, used to flagellate during extreme BDSM play.

Ann Summers

The ultimate girlie night in...

Host an Ann Summers Party, at home and amongst friends, and you'll get:

40% off any sex toy or lingerie set plus 10% of total sales at your party to spend on anything in the Ann Summers catalogue.

To book a party please call **0845 456 2599**
or go to www.annsummers.com/parties

Please quote reference PPM when booking to secure this exclusive discount.